Contents

QUEEN MARY INFANT & NURSERY SCHOOL
CLEETHORPES

INTRODUCTION

THE STORY

Every year Gabriel and the angels celebrate the birth of Jesus by bringing children from around the world to the manger, to tell of their Christmas customs and to offer gifts to the baby Jesus.

The angels are gathered on Christmas Eve. Each has a lucky number on a ticket. Six numbers are chosen from a lucky dip, drawn by Gabriel. The angels with matching numbers are to become messengers and their job is to bring children from countries around the world to visit baby Jesus in the stable. The lucky dip is designed to be conducted like many of the reality shows on TV enjoyed by children today, the winners being announced with great drama and timing (giving even non-speakers the opportunity to react dramatically). The selected messengers receive gold envelopes from Gabriel which contain the name of the country each is to visit.

While the messengers are travelling, the nativity tableau is formed around the manger, ready for their return. As each group of children is brought to the stable, they tell of their special Christmas customs, present a song which reflects their particular country, and make an offering at the manger. In the final scene, children join hands around the manger, to represent peace and hope in the world.

Staging and Rehearsal

The production has been designed to offer an easy way of rehearsing. Each scene stands alone and can be put together at final rehearsals. The groups can be class groups but mixed-age groups would also work if preferred.

There are two points of focus:
- An area for a nativity tableau, containing only the manger during the opening scene.
- An area where the children from around the world illustrate their special customs.

The Initial Stage Set:

The backdrop is a simple starry sky. In the centre of the stage stands the manger. It contains a large round disc of card on which is mounted a map of the world with six countries marked by gold stars. These countries, when plotted on the map, form a rough circle around the world and represent a variety of cultures. The manger also contains the lucky numbers (80, 195, 5, 41, 116, 77) which will be drawn by Gabriel in order to select his messengers.

The cast, except for the angels, is seated in their relevant groups on the floor below the stage area. They need to be ready to access the stage easily when required. For the first and last song, everyone stands to face the audience and sing.

THE Songs

There are nine songs in total, with only the first and last to be learnt by the entire cast. Each national group has a song written in the style of their culture which they need to know well. These group songs can be supported by a choir of angels – the ones not selected to be messengers.

CHRISTMAS TRADITIONS

We've gathered together a few notes on Christmas traditions from the countries featured in the musical. You might like each group to use these as a starting point for further investigation on the countries they are representing in the play and/or inspiration for artwork.

POLAND

Families get together on Christmas Eve to prepare a feast called Wigilia (vigil). The tablecloth is spread over a layer of hay as a reminder of Jesus in the manger, and a place is laid for the Christ child. An even number of dishes must be served, none of which can contain meat, and the meal, which starts with the breaking of a special wafer bread called the 'oplatek', cannot begin until the first star is seen, so the children search the sky hoping to be the first to call out 'Little Star!' (Gwiazdka). The tree is decorated with hand-made cookies and colourfully wrapped chocolate, and a star is placed on the top. Carol singers (Gwiazdory) carry stars and go from house to house throughout the Christmas season, and in some parts of the country it is 'Little Star' who brings gifts for good children.

CHINA

Christians are a minority group in China and they celebrate Christmas with feasts and gifts. The children hang up stockings made of muslin to be filled by Santa, who is known as 'Sheng Dan Lao Ren' (Christmas Old Man). They light their homes with paper lanterns and decorate a Christmas tree with more lanterns, together with paper chains and paper flowers, and call it 'The Tree of Light'. Because Christmas Day is not a holiday in China, the main celebration takes place on Christmas Eve, which is known as 'Ping An Ye' (Silent Night).

AUSTRALIA

It is summertime in Australia at Christmas, but some people still celebrate with turkey, Christmas pudding and all the trimmings. During the gold rush, a small nugget of gold was hidden inside the Christmas pudding, and it was believed that whoever found it would have good luck all year. Nowadays, the nugget is replaced with a charm or trinket, but the finder feels just as lucky! Many people go to the beach for a barbecue and wear Santa hats instead of sun hats, and Bondi beach, visited by thousands each year, is considered the place to be. Santa has been known to arrive on a surfboard!

MALAWI

The focus in Africa is on worship rather than the exchange of gifts, and on singing, dancing and eating together. If gifts can be afforded they will be practical, and children sometimes receive school books or soap. In Malawi, the children make skirts from leaves and prepare home-made instruments. On Christmas Eve they go from house to house in their skirts, singing, dancing and playing their instruments, and will sometimes be given a few coins as a reward. The family feast is meat or fish with maize.

USA

In the United States, the population comes from all over the world and many traditions have been introduced and embraced. The country is renowned for the flamboyant decorations placed outside family homes – some larger than life. Christmas trees are decorated with lights and baubles in the familiar European way, but candy-cane sweet decorations have become an important American tradition during the last 100 years. People now attach meaning to the candy canes:

- They are solid as a rock (God's love)

- They are red for God's love or Jesus' suffering

- They are white for the purity of His birth

- Upside down they make J for Jesus

- The right way up they are like a shepherd's crook. Shepherds came to find Jesus and Jesus is The Good Shepherd

We have chosen Gospel music to represent music from America.

EIRE

In Eire the accent is on worship and making room for the Christ child, and therefore on Christmas Eve families choose a prominent window in the house and leave the curtains open. The youngest member of the family lights a Christmas candle as night falls and places it in the window to shine into the darkness. This light is to guide Mary and Joseph to a safe place to stay, and to make up for the poor welcome they received in Bethlehem. It is also a sign to others that they can be sure of a welcome and will be shown kindness – a stranger at the table is symbolic of making room for Jesus.

Cast List

G [handwritten overlay: 581570 Vicar]

SEVEN ANGEL ... (... king parts with some acting ability. Most can be either boys or girls, ...)

...Angel (hesitant and not confident)

...gel (loves facts and information)

Exc... Angel (inclined to get carried away with enthusiasm)

Fashion Angel (loves to be trendy – probably better suited for a girl)

Bossy Angel (keen, but wants to tell everyone how to do things)

Kind Angel (sensitive and thoughtful)

Smug Angel (very confident, but sadly is not selected this time)

MORE ANGELS — Three to open the play with the first introductory lines. The rest are non-speaking but serve as a supporting choir

NATIVITY TABLEAU (Non-speaking, static. Would suit the youngest children.)

Mary and Joseph

Shepherds

Kings

Star

Angel

CHILDREN FROM AROUND THE WORLD (Have as many children as suits in each group. There are a number of speaking parts in each group, and we've suggested the most suitable ages if you decide to divide your groups by class/age.)

Poland (music and dialogue for younger group)

China (music and dialogue for younger group)

Australia (music and dialogue for middle-age group)

Eire (music and dialogue for middle-age group)

Malawi (music and dialogue for older group)

USA (music and dialogue for older group)

Costume suggestions

GABRIEL/ANGELS   Could be in traditional costumes, but also effective dressed all in white with the addition of small wings. This helps encourage boys to join the ranks and adds diversity to the characterisation (e.g. boys could wear white jeans or trousers with white shirts).

Props:
- 6 gold envelopes for Gabriel
- Large tickets with a number (1 to 195) on each
- Numbers in the manger (80, 195, 5, 41, 116, 77)
- A fashion handbag for Fashion Angel

NATIVITY TABLEAU   Traditional nativity costumes.

CHILDREN OF THE WORLD

Representation of national dress for the children of the world:

Poland   Dark full skirts/trousers, white shirts, waistcoats and colourful ribbons.

Props:
- Christmas bread like a very large wafer, which could be stamped with a nativity scene
- Stars on strings to be held by the children

China   Simple kimono-type wraps, or plain pyjamas, with Chinese hats.

Props:
- Traditionally decorated paper lanterns (lit by torches)
- Strings of paper flowers
- Some muslin stockings

Australia   Beach wear and sun hats or Santa hats.

Props:
- Koala bear
- Sunhat for baby Jesus

Malawi   T-shirts and skirts made from leaves for some, colourful wraps, tunics and T-shirts for others (tie-dye looks good).

Props:
- Home-made instruments including a rattle and drum to present at the manger

USA   Party clothes.

Props:
- Giant red, green and white candy canes.

Eire   Representation of the type of clothes used by boys and girls for Irish dancing.

Props:
- Candles in candlesticks lit by torches
- Matchbox

SCRIPT

Scene 1

(Gabriel and his angels, including the seven potential messenger angels each holding a lucky number, are grouped round the manger which contains the map with six starred countries and the lucky numbers to be selected. Each of the other angels on stage also holds a ticket with a number on it. Gabriel holds six gold envelopes. The entire cast stands to join in the first song.)

ANGEL 1
Talei

Welcome to our Christmas play. Every year, children from Christian countries celebrate the birth of Jesus and each country has its own special Christmas traditions.

ANGEL 2
Sarah-Jayne

We've all been learning about these traditions and would like share some of them with you. Come with us to an imaginary land of angels.

ANGEL 3
Bobbie W

Let's join Gabriel with his angels as they bring children from all around the world to meet each other at the manger, tell of their customs and offer gifts to the baby Jesus. Are you ready? Gabriel's calling!

Song 1.   GABRIEL CALLING   CD track 1/10

GABRIEL
Holly W

I see you have each chosen your numbers for the lucky dip – well done!

There are six countries selected this Christmas Eve, and the six angels whose numbers are drawn from the manger will be our special Christmas messengers who will fly off to visit those countries. Good luck everyone!

ANGELS

(Make excited noises and wave their tickets) Ooooooh! Can't wait! What fun!

BOSSY ANGEL
Mischa

(Hands on hips) So listen everyone, if your number comes up, don't mess about! Fly quickly to the country you are given and bring the children back here. It's a really important job, you know!

HOPEFUL ANGEL
Megan

I wonder who it will be. I would so love to go!

EXCITED ANGEL
Grace

(Bouncing up and down and waving ticket) I've got my favourite number. Look – number 5!

CLEVER ANGEL
Lucy

(Seriously) And I've got number 195. I think that's the highest number. I wonder if that's how many countries there are in the world. I think I'll go and do some research.

FASHION ANGEL
Paige

(Twirling with her handbag) Mine is number 80, but I've put it safely into my new bag. Do you like it? I made it to match my wings!

SMUG ANGEL
Gracie-mae

(Confidently) I always get lucky! Last year I went to Canada, the year before that Hawaii, and the year before that it was ...

BOSSY ANGEL
Mischa

(Interrupting) Well, good old you! But just remember that not everyone here has been that lucky!

HOPEFUL ANGEL
Megan

(Timidly) Like me! I do hope my number is drawn this year. See? I've got 77 – it does sound kind of lucky, don't you think?

KIND ANGEL
~~Sophie~~
Robyn

(Giving Hopeful Angel a hug) I really hope you are chosen! Once, I was lucky

8

and went to fetch children from Mexico. It was such fun! I always watch over them now – they're sort of special to me.

CLEVER ANGEL
Lucy

All children are special – they are the future of the world and we must watch over every one of them!

GABRIEL
Holly W

(With great ceremony, not unlike announcements on TV talent shows) Now for the Lucky Dip! Who will our messengers be tonight? *(Dramatic pause, then Gabriel puts his hand in the manger and draws out number 80)*

GABRIEL

We have number … number 80!

FASHION ANGEL
Paige

Oh! I do believe that's me – I'll just look in my new bag. Yes! Fantastic! *(She gives a twirl as she receives a gold envelope from Gabriel)*

(Gabriel dips again and picks 195.)

GABRIEL
Holly

Number 195!

CLEVER ANGEL
Lucy

Oh thanks, that's me! *(Takes the gold envelope from Gabriel)* As soon as I know which country I've got, I'll study the map and plan my route!

GABRIEL
Holly W

(Dips again and picks 5) Number 5!

EXCITED ANGEL
Grace

(Bouncing over to get the envelope) Oh, how exciting! I told you 5 was my favourite number!

GABRIEL
Holly W

(Dips and picks 41) Number 41!

KIND ANGEL
Sophie Robyn

(To Hopeful Angel) Oh, that's me. Now I feel bad – I've been chosen before. Here, have my ticket – I'd love you to go instead!

GABRIEL
Holly

(Firmly) Tickets are NOT transferable!

(Kind Angel looks sadly at Hopeful and mouths 'sorry'. Hopeful smiles sadly and mouths 'never mind!' Then Kind takes the envelope.)

GABRIEL

(Dips again and calls 116) Number 116!

BOSSY ANGEL
Mischa

(Bustling forward importantly) That'll be me then! Now, I must get myself organised! What time do we leave? *(Takes the envelope and with great fuss joins the others selected)*

ALL

Shh!!!!!!!

(Gabriel becomes very theatrical, making his last announcement with drama and long pauses)

GABRIEL
Holly

And now … there is just one envelope left! … And the last messenger chosen tonight, to find out how the children of the world celebrate Christmas, is …

SMUG ANGEL
Gracie-mae

I bet it's me again!

HOPEFUL ANGEL
megan

(Whispers and raises her eyes to heaven) Please! Please! Please!

GABRIEL
Holly W

(Holding up 77, the last ticket) Number 77!

HOPEFUL ANGEL
megan D

I can't believe it – it's me! *(Takes the envelope)* Thank you so, so much!

GABRIEL *Holly*	Now, will all our messengers please step forward. Come along, stand over here with your envelopes. One by one, you will open your envelope and see which countries the children are coming from this year. Then you must leave.
SMUG ANGEL *Gracie-mae*	I know just how exciting it is. Did I tell you that last year I went to …
GABRIEL *Holly*	*(Interrupting and pointing to Hopeful)* We'll start with you.

(Hopeful Angel opens her/his envelope, points to the country on the map as s/he says it and flies off to join her/his group of children. Then each of the others goes through the same routine.)

HOPEFUL ANGEL *megan*	Poland!
CLEVER ANGEL *Lucy*	China! Now that IS a big country!
EXCITED ANGEL *Grace*	Australia!
FASHION ANGEL *Paige*	Malawi!
BOSSY ANGEL *Mischa*	The United States of America!
KIND ANGEL *~~Sophie~~ Robyn*	Eire – that's Ireland – how lovely!

(The angels wave and call goodbye, and then form a choir to support the singing that follows.)

Scene 2

(The nativity tableau is built up around the manger as the following song is sung and then remains centre stage until the end of the play. During the song the star leads the way. One of the extra angels carries the baby to the stage during the first verse, followed by Mary and Joseph, who are given the baby and take their places by the manger. The shepherds and kings take their places during the second verse.)

GABRIEL *Holly*	*(To the audience)* Before the messengers return with the children, I want you all to remember that first Christmas and welcome the baby Jesus once again.

Song 2.   ALLELUIA   CD track 2/11

(During a reprise of the music for 'Alleluia' (use backing track 11), Hopeful Angel returns with the children from Poland, each carrying a star twirling on a string or on a stick. One carries a disc of bread. This bread is traditionally a large type of wafer and could be made from card. Sometimes it is stamped with a nativity scene.)

HOPEFUL ANGEL *megan D*	Here we are – I hope I did my job well! Look, I've brought children all the way from Poland and they've been real little stars!

(The Polish children address the audience with the following lines.)

CHILD 1 *Bartosh*	Stars are an important part of Christmas in Poland.

(The children wave their stars.)

CHILD 2 *Jay*	Do you like the stars we've made?
CHILD 3 *~~olivia~~ Ella*	We always put a big star on top of our Christmas tree as well!
CHILD 4 *~~Charlie D~~* *Carmen*	At home, everything is ready for the celebration. The table has been laid for the Christmas Eve feast.

CHILD 5
~~Carmen~~
Charlie D

And we always put some hay under the tablecloth to remind us that Jesus was born in a stable.

CHILD 6
Kaizer

We even lay an extra place for Him at the table!

CHILD 7
Owen F

But the feast cannot begin until the first star has been seen in the sky.

CHILD 8
Scarlett

Children all over Poland will watch the sky tonight hoping to be the one that sees the first star.

CHILD 9
Zach

We have a name for that star, it's Gwiazdka, which means Little Star.

CHILD 10
~~Ella~~ Olivia

I hope it's me!

(They stare up at the sky during the intro of their song, pointing excitedly.)

Song 3.   LITTLE STAR   CD track 3/12

(The children turn towards the manger.)

CHILD 1
Bartosh

Little Jesus, these stars will shine in your stable.

CHILD 2
Jay

(Presents bread) We've brought this special Christmas bread to share with you.

(They turn towards the audience.)

CHILD 3
~~Olivia~~ Ella

When the feast is over, we will gather round the Christmas tree to sing carols and tell stories.

CHILD 4
~~Charlie D~~ Carmen

And if we have been good, there will be gifts for us from Gwiazdka – Little Star.

ALL

Wesolych swiat bozego narodzenia!
Happy Christmas!

(During a reprise of the song (CD track 12), two children make their presentation and take their places in the tableau. Hopeful Angel remains on stage and the rest of the group return to their places.

Clever Angel enters with children from China. They are carrying strings of paper flower decorations and lanterns, also made of paper, which would be most effective if lit in some way with torches. Some carry muslin stockings.)

CLEVER ANGEL
Lucy

Here are the children from China – they have taught me so much! And they are very clever. They make fantastic things out of paper!

CHILD 1
Alysha

We make our tree beautiful each year with decorations made of paper, like these.

CHILD 2
Tony

See, we've made strings of pretty paper flowers.

CHILD 3
Gracie

But the best decorations are the paper lanterns which light up the tree.

CHILD 4
Kairah

We call our Christmas tree 'The Tree of Light'.

CHILD 5
Harry P

We welcome Jesus with light because He brought light to the world.

11

Song 4. THE TREE OF LIGHT CD track 4/13

(During the song they process and sing with a sequence of movement in the middle section. Have some fun getting the children to help choreograph this.)

(They turn towards the manger.)

CHILD 1 Little Jesus we have come to worship you.
Alysha
CHILD 2 We've brought you gifts of lanterns and flowers.
Tony
(They turn towards the audience.)

CHILD 3 *(Holding up a muslin stocking)* Tonight we will hang up our stockings. See?
Gracie They are made of muslin.

CHILD 4 And who knows what lovely things we will find in them on Christmas
Kairah morning!

ALL Sheng dan kuai le!
Happy Christmas!

(During a reprise of the song (CD track 13), two children make their presentation and take their place in the tableau. Clever Angel remains on stage and the rest of the group return to their places.

Excited Angel enters with the children from Australia dressed for the beach. One carries a sun hat, another a koala.)

EXCITED ANGEL I have had such fun with this lot! They are the children from Australia. You'll
Grace never believe what they do at Christmas!

CHILD 1 G'day! We're off to the beach tomorrow for a Christmas Barbie!
Paige B
CHILD 2 Y'see, Christmas is right in the middle of our summer holidays!
Melissa
CHILD 3 So we spend Christmas Day playing in the hot sun.
Noah
CHILD 4 But we still decorate our tree with artificial snow and wear Santa hats
Riley instead of sunhats! *(S/he demonstrates)*

CHILD 5 And we still tuck into turkey and Christmas pud!
Keegan
CHILD 6 And of course, we hang our stockings up for Santa, though he must feel
Samuel extremely hot here in his thick red coat!

CHILD 7 It's great singing carols on the beach! What do you think of this one?
Joshua
E-D **Song 5. CHRISTMAS DAY ON THE BEACH, BOYS** CD track 5/14

(They turn towards the manger.)

CHILD 1 Baby Jesus, we have come to find you on Christmas Eve.
Paige B
CHILD 2 And just look, I've brought you a hat to protect you from the sun.
Melissa
CHILD 3 And I've brought a koala for you to cuddle when life gets scary!
Noah
(All turn towards the audience.)

CHILD 4 Riley	Shall I let you into a secret? This year we'll all be keeping an eye on the surf, because the rumour is that Santa is ditching his sleigh and arriving on a surfboard instead!
ALL	That's so cool! Happy Christmas everyone!

(During a reprise of the song (CD track 14), two children make their presentation and join the tableau. Excited Angel remains on stage and the rest of the group return to their places. Fashion Angel enters with children from Malawi. Some are wearing skirts made from leaves, others bright cotton wraps or tunics. Some carry home-made instruments.)

FASHION ANGEL Paige Lee	Here are the children from Malawi – don't they look just great? They made these skirts themselves. I reckon you could easily make a bag to match!
CHILD 1 Chloe	We have been busy for days making our Christmas skirts from leaves. We make them every year. *(They give a twirl)*
CHILD 2 Abigail	We have been making our instruments too, and rehearsing songs and Christmas music. In Malawi we love to sing and dance.
CHILD 3 Millie	On Christmas Eve we go from door to door singing Christmas songs and playing music for our neighbours.
CHILD 4 Paisley	Sometimes they are so impressed that they give us a coin or two. See what you think!

Song 6.   KUYIMBA   **CD track 6/15-16**

(They turn towards the manger.)

CHILD 1 ~~Chloe~~ Connor	Little Jesus, we are not rich like the kings. We do not have gold, frankincense or myrrh to offer you, but instead we give you our voices.
CHILD 2 Cole ~~Abigail~~	And we have made you a drum and a rattle – birthday gifts for a very special child.

(They turn towards the audience.)

CHILD 3 Millie	Tomorrow on Christmas Day, we will all feast together on meat, fish and maize and retell the story of that first Christmas.
CHILD 4 Charlie ~~Paisley~~ R	We will sing and make Christmas music together.
ALL	Khilisimasi Yabwino! Happy Christmas!

(During a reprise of the song (CD track 15), two children make their presentation and take their place in the tableau. Fashion Angel remains on stage and the rest of the group return to their places. Bossy Angel enters with children from the USA. They carry large walking-stick candy canes of red, green and white.)

BOSSY ANGEL Mischa	This way everyone! Spread out now, and remember to speak clearly so that everyone can hear what you have to say.
CHILD 1 Rhiannon	We've been getting ready for Christmas for weeks! Our houses are decorated inside and out!
CHILD 2 Ava	The front lawn is lit up with enormous decorations, there's a huge Santa on the roof and the Christmas tree has been brought into the house.

CHILD 3 *Alfie D*	The fairy is on the very top of the tree.
CHILD 4 *Owen K*	And the fairy lights are working perfectly! They all lit up first go … thank goodness!
CHILD 5 *Connor H*	There are baubles and tinsel and stars on every branch.
CHILD 6 *Damon*	And of course – we haven't forgotten the candy canes!

(They hold up their red, green and white striped sticks.)

CHILD 7 *Jon-Paul*	Upside down, they remind us that J is for Jesus! *(They demonstrate)*
CHILD 8 *Kieran*	The right way up, they remind us that the shepherds who ran to find Jesus in the stable, carried crooks. *(They demonstrate again)*
CHILD 9 *Ethan*	And we call Jesus 'The Good Shepherd' because he looks after us all.
CHILD 10 *Robyn*	All we need now is our gospel choir!

Song 7.   COME TO THE MANGER   CD track 7/17-18

(They turn towards the manger.)

CHILD 1 *Rhiannon*	Jesus, we've heard the good news and have come to the manger.
CHILD 2 *Ava*	We've brought you some candy canes because you are Jesus, The Good Shepherd who watches over us all.

(They turn towards the audience.)

CHILD 3 *Alfie*	American Christians come from all over the world and so we have many different traditions in our country. But we all love celebrating the birth of Jesus, our shepherd and our friend.
ALL	Happy Christmas everyone. Have a nice day!

(During a reprise of the song (CD track 17), two children make their presentation and join the tableau. Bossy Angel remains on stage and the rest of the group return to their places. Kind Angel enters with children from Eire. Some carry candles.)

KIND ANGEL *Sophie*	Here come the children from Eire. They have such a lovely Irish tradition to tell you about, haven't you children?
CHILD 1 *Georgia*	Yes, it's all about a guiding light. This is the light that we will put in our window tonight.
CHILD 2 *Chelsea*	We will put it where everyone passing can see it.
CHILD 3 *Kacy*	When it gets dark, the youngest child in the family will light the candle.
CHILD 4 *Bailey*	The twinkling light will show Mary and Joseph that we are waiting to welcome them into our house if they pass our way.
CHILD 5 *Ryan E*	We won't say, 'No room!' and turn them away.
CHILD 6 *Kieran J*	The light is a signal to travellers and lonely people as well.

CHILD 7	It tells them that they are welcome to come in and share all the good things we have.
Georgia	
CHILD 8	*(Holding the matchbox)* So come on Patrick, you are the youngest child here tonight. Be very careful as you light the Christmas candle to shine in the darkness.
Kieran J	

(Patrick 'lights' the candle (powered by a torch), and the other children switch on theirs as well.)

Song 8.   CHRISTMAS CANDLE   CD track 8/19

(They turn towards the manger.)

CHILD 1	Baby Jesus, we will always make room for you. Here are some candles to light up your stable.
Georgia	
CHILD 2	Help us to shine like bright candles in the night and be really good this Christmas.
Chelsea	

(They turn towards the audience.)

CHILD 3	Tonight I will go to sleep really quickly so that Santa can come early and get back home to his warm bed!
Kacy	
ALL	Nollaig Shona!
	Happy Christmas!

(During a reprise of the song (CD track 19), two children make their presentation and join the tableau. The rest go back to their places ready for the finale. Kind Angel joins Gabriel and the other messenger angels , who step forward.)

EXCITED ANGEL	Isn't it exciting that there are so many ways to celebrate Christmas?
Grace Allard	
CLEVER ANGEL	Yes – so many interesting traditions from all around the world!
Lucy	
BOSSY ANGEL	And then, don't forget that each family, within each country, has its own way of celebrating as well!
Mischa	
FASHION ANGEL	Isn't it wonderful that we are all so different?
Paige	
SMUG ANGEL	And wonderful that we are all so much the same!
Gracie -mae	
KIND ANGEL	Yes, we have all heard the same Christmas message.
Sophie	
HOPEFUL ANGEL	And we all celebrate the birth of the same very special baby!
megan	
GABRIEL	So let's join hands around the world and give the baby Jesus a birthday gift of love and hope for children everywhere.
Holly W	

(The entire cast stands to face the audience and holds hands. The twelve children who have remained on stage from the six countries encircle the manger and join hands.)

| ALL | Happy Christmas! *(This is shouted in all the languages used in the play, to create a loud and multilingual greeting in unison.)* |

Song 9.   CHILDREN OF THE WORLD   CD track 9/20

Gabriel Calling

Words and Music by
Mary Green and Julie Stanley

With energy ♩ = 148

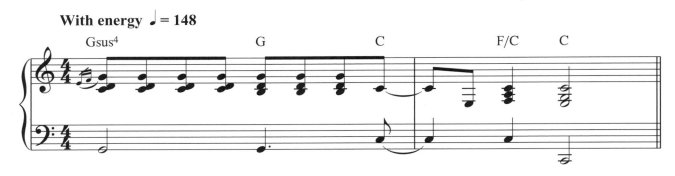

(a tempo *2nd time***)**

Ga - bri - el call - ing, call-ing all an - gels, stars are shi - ning

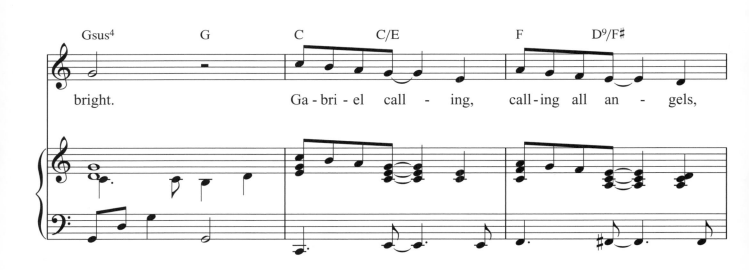

bright.   Ga - bri - el call - ing, call-ing all an - gels,

Alleluia

Words and Music by
Mary Green and Julie Stanley

1. Here is the
2. Here are the

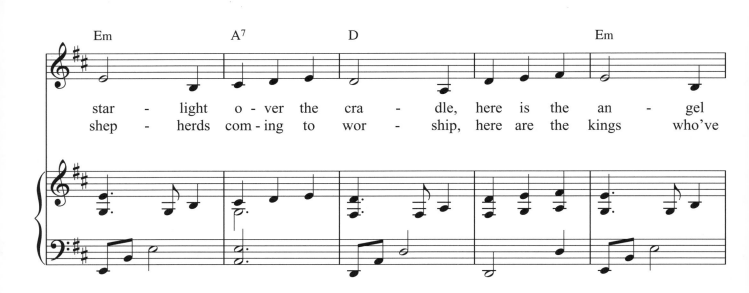

star - light o - ver the cra - dle, here is the an - gel
shep - herds com - ing to wor - ship, here are the kings who've

wait - ing to sing,   here is the ba - by born in a
fol - lowed the star,   here are the chil - dren guid - ed by

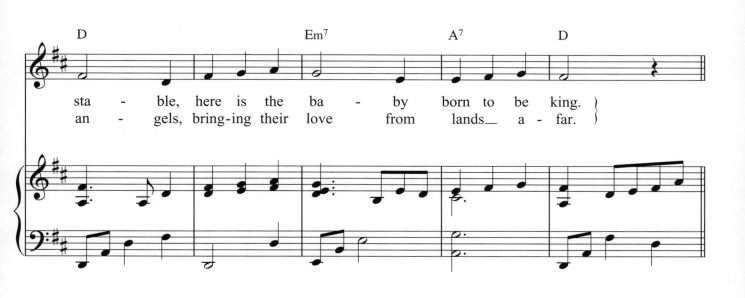

sta - ble, here is the ba - by born to be king.)
an - gels, bring-ing their love from lands— a - far.)

Angel solo

Al - le - lu - ia, al - le - lu - ia, al - le -

Little Star
(Poland)

Words and Music by
Mary Green and Julie Stanley

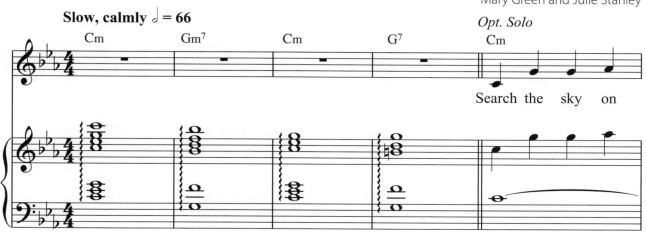

Search the sky on

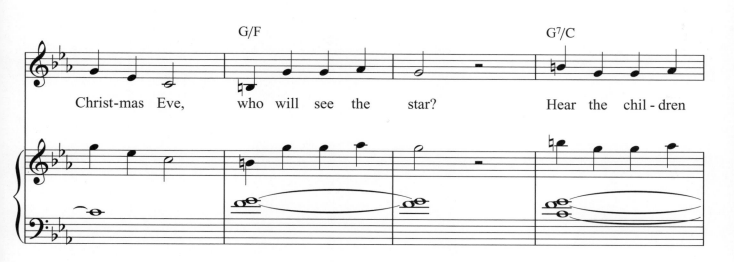

Christ-mas Eve, who will see the star? Hear the chil-dren

laugh and shout, *(spoken)* COME OUT! Wherever you are.

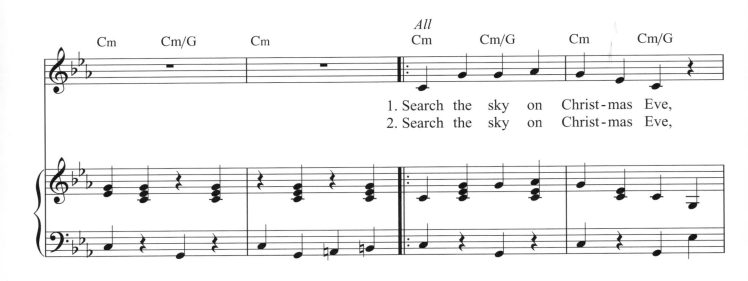

1. Search the sky on Christ-mas Eve,
2. Search the sky on Christ-mas Eve,

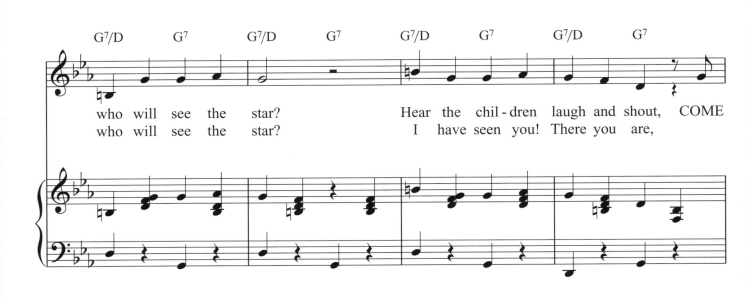

who will see the star? Hear the chil-dren laugh and shout, COME
who will see the star? I have seen you! There you are,

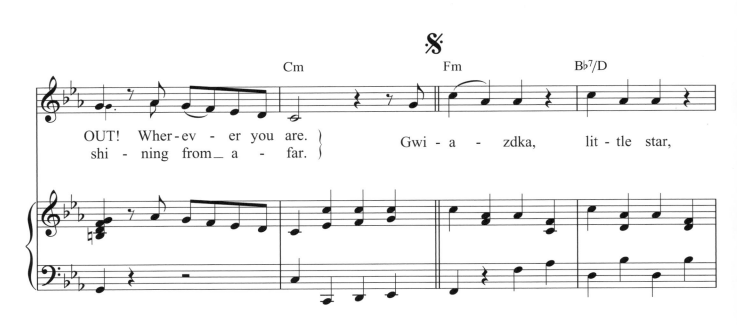

OUT! Wher-ev - er you are. }
shi - ning from_ a - far. }   Gwi - a - zdka,   lit - tle star,

shine your gol - den light. Gwi - a - zdka, lit - tle star,

bless our feast to - night.

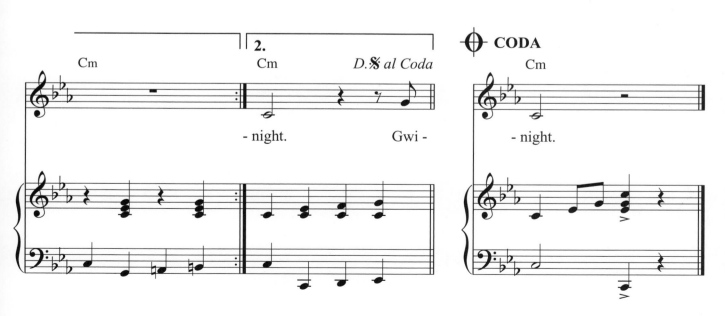

- night. Gwi -

- night.

THE TREE OF LIGHT

(China)

Words and Music by
Mary Green and Julie Stanley

Steadily ♩ = 62

De-co-rate the tree of light, with our lan-terns burn-ing bright, wel-com-ing the new-born king to - night. Lit-tle Je-sus in the hay, born for us on Christ-mas Day, let our Christ-mas lan-terns light your

Dance interlude

way.

1. **2.**

Lit-tle Je-sus, ti - ny king, you are Lord of ev - ery-thing.

rit.

Hear our Christ-mas ca - rols as we sing.

Christmas Day On The Beach, Boys
(Australia)

Words and Music by
Mary Green and Julie Stanley

1. Christ-mas Day on the beach, boys, Christ-mas Day in the sun. *(Clap, clap)*
2. Ba - by born in a sta - ble, down in Pa - les - tine.

We are hav-ing a bar - bie, we are hav-ing some fun. *(Clap, clap)*
He knows all a-bout sand, man, so we're do-ing just fine.

Wel-come ba - by Je - sus, born in Beth - le - hem,

Kuyimba
(Malawi)

Words and Music by
Mary Green and Julie Stanley

Always building ♩ = 100

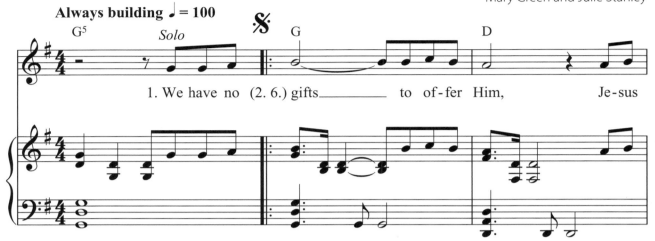

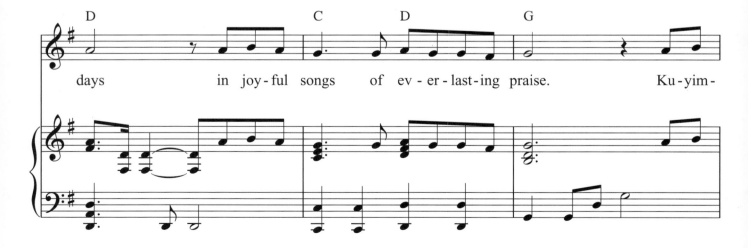

34

Come to the Manger
(USA)

Words and Music by
Mary Green and Julie Stanley

Lively ♩ = 154

1. Come to the man - ger on Christ-mas Eve, al - le -
2. Come to the man - ger you shep - herds and kings, al - le -

-lu - ia. Come to the man - ger, all
-lu - ia. Come to the man - ger on

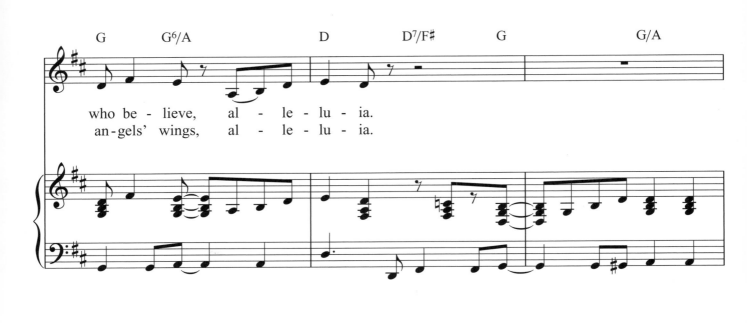

who be - lieve, al - le - lu - ia.
an - gels' wings, al - le - lu - ia.

God has sent his own Son down,_____
Come and join the gos - pel choir,_____

spread the mes - sage all a - round,_____
raise your voi - ces high - er and high - er,

there's a new king in town!
we can set the world on fire!

Al - le - lu - ia,
Al - le - lu - ia,

al - le - lu - ia.
al - le -

-lu - ia.

3. Come to the man - ger from

CHRISTMAS CANDLE
(EIRE)

Words and Music by
Mary Green and Julie Stanley

In a flowing style ♪ = 140

1. Light a can - dle to shine in the dark - ness,___ guid - ing
(2.) can - dle to shine in the win - dow,___ to___
(3.) can - dle to shine in the dark - ness,___ with its

Ma - ry and Jo - seph this way, light a can - dle to send out the
chase a - way fear and des - pair, light a can - dle to send out the
ti - ny but po - wer - ful light, light a can - dle to send out the

mes-sage,_ 'Come_ in, you are wel-come to stay.'
mes-sage,_ 'We have plen-ty of kind-ness to share.'
mes-sage,_ 'Christ_ Je-sus was born on this night.'

Christ-mas can-dle, guid-ing light, Christ-mas can-dle burn-ing

bright.

2. Light a burn-ing bright.
3. Light a

CHILDREN OF THE WORLD

Words and Music by
Mary Green and Julie Stanley

Gabriel Calling

ANGEL 3:   *Are you ready? Gabriel's calling!*

CHORUS   *Gabriel calling, calling all angels,*
Stars are shining bright.
Gabriel calling, calling all angels,
Gather round the manger tonight.

Messengers flying high, into the Christmas sky,
Travel to lands far and near.
Messengers flying high, into the Christmas sky,
Bringing children here to worship.

CHORUS   *Gabriel calling, calling all angels,*
Stars are shining bright.
Gabriel calling, calling all angels,
Gather round the manger tonight.
Gather round the manger tonight.

Words and Music by Mary Green and Julie Stanley
© 2010 Out of the Ark Ltd, Middlesex TW12 2HD
CCLI Song No. 5725564

Alleluia

GABRIEL: *Before the messengers return with the children, I want you all to remember that first Christmas and welcome the baby Jesus once again.*

All

1   Here is the starlight over the cradle,
Here is the angel waiting to sing,
Here is the baby born in a stable,
Here is the baby born to be king.

Angel solo

Alleluia, alleluia, alleluia, alleluia.

All

Alleluia, alleluia, alleluia, alleluia.

2   Here are the shepherds coming to worship,
Here are the kings who've followed the star,
Here are the children guided by angels,
Bringing their love from lands afar.
Alleluia, alleluia, alleluia, alleluia.
Alleluia, alleluia, alleluia, alleluia.

Words and Music by Mary Green and Julie Stanley
© 2010 Out of the Ark Ltd, Middlesex TW12 2HD
CCLI Song No. 5725612

LITTLE STAR

(POLAND)

CHILD 10:   *I hope it's me!*

Optional Solo
Search the sky on Christmas Eve,
Who will see the star?
Hear the children laugh and shout,
(Spoken) COME OUT! Wherever you are.

All

1   Search the sky on Christmas Eve,
Who will see the star?
Hear the children laugh and shout,
COME OUT! Wherever you are.

CHORUS   *Gwiazdka – little star,*
Shine your golden light.
Gwiazdka – little star,
Bless our feast tonight.

2   Search the sky on Christmas Eve,
Who will see the star?
I have seen you! There you are,
Shining from afar.

CHORUS x 2

Words and Music by Mary Green and Julie Stanley
© 2010 Out of the Ark Ltd, Middlesex TW12 2HD
CCLI Song No. 5725636

THE TREE OF LIGHT

(CHIna)

CHILD 5: *We welcome Jesus with light because He brought light to the world.*

Decorate the tree of light,
With our lanterns burning bright,
Welcoming the newborn king tonight.
Little Jesus in the hay,
Born for us on Christmas Day,
Let our Christmas lanterns light your way.

(Dance interlude, with lanterns & flowers)

Little Jesus, tiny king,
You are Lord of everything.
Hear our Christmas carols as we sing.

Words and Music by Mary Green and Julie Stanley
© 2010 Out of the Ark Ltd, Middlesex TW12 2HD
CCLI Song No. 5725643

CHRISTMAS Day On THE BEACH, Boys

(Australia)

CHILD 7:   *It's great singing carols on the beach! What do you think of this one?*

1   Christmas Day on the beach, boys,
     Christmas Day in the sun. *(Clap, clap)*
     We are having a barbie,
     We are having some fun. *(Clap, clap)*

     CHORUS   *Welcome baby Jesus,*
                     Born in Bethlehem,
                     Born to bring the message,
                     Peace and love to all men.

2   Baby born in a stable,
     Down in Palestine. *(Clap, clap)*
     He knows all about sand, man,
     So we're doing just fine. *(Clap, clap)*

     CHORUS x 2

Words and Music by Mary Green and Julie Stanley
© 2010 Out of the Ark Ltd, Middlesex TW12 2HD
CCLI Song No. 5725667

Kuyimba

(Malawi)

CHILD 4:   *Sometimes they are so impressed that they give us a coin or two. See what you think!*

We have no gifts to offer Him,
Jesus Christ our baby King.
We will serve Him all our days
In joyful songs of everlasting praise.

Kuyimba, kuyimba, kuyimba.

1st time – solo
2nd time – all
3rd – 5th times, add new harmony per verse
6th time – solo

If you are working with younger children who may find the harmony parts too demanding, you can use the backing track with added backing vocals (CD track 16) and sing the melody throughout.

Words and Music by Mary Green and Julie Stanley
© 2010 Out of the Ark Ltd, Middlesex TW12 2HD
CCLI Song No. 5725674

Come To The Manger
(usa)

CHILD 10:   *All we need now is our gospel choir!*

1   Come to the manger on Christmas Eve, alleluia.
      Come to the manger, all who believe, alleluia.
      God has sent his own Son down,
      Spread the message all around,
      There's a new king in town! Alleluia, alleluia.

2   Come to the manger you shepherds and kings, alleluia.
      Come to the manger on angels' wings, alleluia.
      Come and join the gospel choir,
      Raise your voices higher and higher,
      We can set the world on fire! Alleluia, alleluia.

3   Come to the manger from every land, alleluia, *(alleluia)*.
      Come to the manger o'er sea and sand, alleluia, *(alleluia)*.
      Come and worship here today, *(oh yeah, yeah, yeah)*
      Kneel before the King and pray, *(oh yeah, yeah)*
      Join together now and say,
      Alleluia *(alleluia)*, alleluia *(alleluia)*,
      Alleluia.

Have some fun working out choreography for this number to really give it a celebratory gospel feel. Also, if you are working with younger children who may find the backing vocals too demanding, you can use the backing track with the added vocals (CD track 18).

Words and Music by Mary Green and Julie Stanley
© 2010 Out of the Ark Ltd, Middlesex TW12 2HD
CCLI Song No. 5725698

CHRISTMAS CANDLE
(EIRE)

CHILD 8: *So come on Patrick, you are the youngest child here tonight. Be very careful as you light the Christmas candle to shine in the darkness.*

1 Light a candle to shine in the darkness,
   Guiding Mary and Joseph this way,
   Light a candle to send out the message,
   'Come in, you are welcome to stay.'

   CHORUS *Christmas candle, guiding light,*
   Christmas candle burning bright.

2 Light a candle to shine in the window,
   To chase away fear and despair,
   Light a candle to send out the message,
   'We have plenty of kindness to share.'

   CHORUS

3 Light a candle to shine in the darkness,
   With its tiny but powerful light,
   Light a candle to send out the message,
   'Christ Jesus was born on this night.'

   CHORUS

Words and Music by Mary Green and Julie Stanley
© 2010 Out of the Ark Ltd, Middlesex TW12 2HD
CCLI Song No. 5725715

CHILDREN OF THE WORLD

ALL: *Happy Christmas !*

CHORUS *Children of the world celebrate Christmas,*
Children of the world wherever you are,
Children of the world singing together,
Make the light of hope shine like a star.

Join together,
Let our hands circle the earth,
Join together,
Celebrate Jesus' birth.

CHORUS *Children of the world celebrate Christmas,*
Children of the world wherever you are,
Children of the world singing together,
Make the light of hope shine like a star,
Shine like a star,
Wherever you are,
Children of the world.

Words and Music by Mary Green and Julie Stanley
© 2010 Out of the Ark Ltd, Middlesex TW12 2HD
CCLI Song No. 5725722

Licence Application Form

(Children Of The World)

If you perform **Children Of The World** to an audience other than children and staff you will need to photocopy and complete this form and return it by post or fax to Out of the Ark Music in order to apply for a licence. If anticipated audience sizes are very small or if special circumstances apply please contact Out of the Ark Music.

The licence will permit the holder to:

- Perform *Children Of The World* on the dates applied for.
- Reproduce the lyrics to the songs on printed paper, such as for programmes, and to make transparencies for overhead projection. The following credit should be included: *'Reproduced by kind permission © Out of the Ark Ltd'.*
- Photocopy the script for learning purposes. Copies must be destroyed after the performance.
- Make no more than two copies of the music, to be used by participating musicians on the performance dates.

If the performance is to be recorded please contact Out of the Ark Music.

We wish to apply for a licence to perform *Children Of The World* by Mary Green and Julie Stanley

Customer number (if known): ....

Name of school / organisation: ....

Name of organiser / producer: ....

Date(s) of performance(s): ....

Invoice address: ....

....

Post code: .... **Country:** ....

Telephone number: ....

Number of performances (excl. dress rehearsal)	Performances without admission charges	Performances with admission charges
1	☐ **£14.40*** [€18.75]	☐ **£19.20** [€25.00]
2	☐ **£19.20** [€25.00]	☐ **£24.00** [€31.20]
3 or more	☐ **£24.00** [€31.20]	☐ **£30.13** [€39.20]

Tick one of the boxes above.

☐ Tick here to receive licensing information for any audio or video recording of a performance.

Tick one of the four payment options below: (Invoices will be sent with all licences)

☐ Please bill my school/nursery at the above address (UK schools/nurseries only)

☐ I enclose a cheque (Pounds Sterling) for £ .... payable to Out of the Ark Music

☐ I enclose a cheque (Euro) for € .... payable to Out of the Ark Music

☐ Please charge the following card: (Visa [not Electron], MasterCard & Maestro accepted)

Card No ....

Start Date _ _ / _ _ (MM/YY)   Expiry Date _ _ / _ _ (MM/YY)   3 digit security code: _ _ _ (last 3 digits on signature strip)

Address: Out of the Ark Music   Phone: +44 (0)20 8481 7200
             Kingsway Business Park   Fax: +44 (0)20 8941 5548
             Oldfield Road   Email: info@outoftheark.com
             Hampton
             Middlesex TW12 2HD
             United Kingdom

*The licence fees shown on this form are for 2011-2012 and include VAT at 20%. Prices may be subject to revision. Customers outside the EU will NOT be charged VAT.

COPYRIGHT & LICENSING – WHAT YOU NEED TO KNOW

The world of copyright and licensing can seem very daunting, particularly because there is an obligation on schools to comply with copyright law. We're here to help you through the process and to keep you legal. The guidelines below explain the most common copyright and licensing issues.

Staging THIS Musical

Performing this musical to an audience (other than pupils and staff) requires a performance licence.

** Please note that your Performing Rights Society (PRS) Licence does NOT cover musicals**

We issue affordable performance licences to schools, churches and nurseries. To apply, simply complete the performance licence application form on page 54 and fax or post it to us.

The performance licence will permit the holder to:
- Perform the musical on the dates applied for.
- Reproduce the song lyrics on printed paper, e.g. for programmes, to make transparencies for overhead projection and to display the lyrics on an interactive whiteboard or other type of screen. The following credit should be included with the lyrics:
  'Reproduced by kind permission © Out of the Ark Ltd'
- Photocopy the script for learning purposes. Copies must be destroyed after the performance.
- Make up to two photocopies of the music score for use by participating musicians on the performance dates.
- Play the CD (either backing tracks or vocal tracks) at the performance.

Putting On A Concert

If you are not staging this musical but are performing any of our songs for the public on school premises (i.e. to anyone other than pupils or staff) then royalty payments become due. Contact Out of the Ark Music directly to obtain a licence. **Please note:** There is no need to obtain a licence from the publisher if your school has an arrangement with the **Performing Rights Society (PRS)** either directly or through the local authority.

Making an Audio Recording or a Video of the Performance

If you wish to make an audio or video recording of your performance of any of our works please visit www.outoftheark.com/licensing for further information.

Singing Songs In THE Classroom

You are free to use all of the material – including songs and scripts – in the classroom for teaching purposes. If photocopying any part of the book for teaching purposes please record this usage on your school's photocopy log to ensure that you are legally protected.

Singing Songs In an Assembly or In Church

Songs may be sung in assembly without charge. In addition the CD may be played provided that your school has a PRS licence. However, the reproduction of the lyrics and/or musical scores for use in an assembly or a church requires a licence. The following licences from Christian Copyright Licensing Limited (www.ccli.com) permit the photocopying or reproduction of song lyrics or musical scores – for example to create song sheets, overhead transparencies or to display the lyrics or music using any electronic display medium:

> **For UK schools:** A Collective Worship Copyright Licence and a Music Reproduction Licence
> **For churches:** A Church Copyright and Music Reproduction Licence

Please ensure that you log the songs that are used on your CCLI and MRL copy report.

Organisations that do not hold one of the above licences should contact Out of the Ark Limited directly for permission.

Your CCLI licence also grants you permission to display the song lyrics from our Words on Screen™ CD ROMs on a whiteboard or other screen. Simply log the song titles on your copy report.

Copying and File-sharing

Copying Out of the Ark Music's audio CDs is not permitted without obtaining a licence from the publisher. Installation of Out of the Ark Music's audio CD tracks on to a computer is strictly forbidden without a licence – we can provide schools with a 'Learning Platform Installation Licence'. File-sharing of any of our audio tracks or CD ROM files is strictly prohibited. For more information visit **www.outoftheark.com/licensing**.

Helpful information can be found on the following website:

A Guide to Licensing Copyright in Schools: www.outoftheark.com/licensing

And remember, we are always happy to help. For advice simply contact our customer services team:

Tel: +44 (0)20 8481 7200
Email: copyright@outoftheark.com

OUT OF THE ARK **ESSENTIALS**

CHRISTMAS CAROLS

A stunning collection of 20 of your favourite carols for singing in school, church or at any Christmas gathering. Carefully compiled to include a mix of the best carols ranging from absolute classics to modern favourites, this folio is 'essential' for any school, at any Christmas!

Every carol has been arranged to suit primary aged children and is presented with high quality recordings for which Out of the Ark Music is renowned.

Titles Comprise:

Joy To The World
Calypso Carol
Go, Tell It On The Mountain
O Come All Ye Faithful
Infant Holy
Mary's Boy Child
O Little Town Of Bethlehem
Ding Dong! Merrily On High
It Was On A Starry Night
Hark! The Herald Angels Sing

The Zither Carol
Away In A Manger
We Three Kings Of Orient Are
In The Bleak Midwinter
The Little Drummer Boy
Angels From The Realms Of Glory
While Shepherds Watched
Silent Night
Once In Royal David's City
The First Nowell

Out of the Ark Music
Kingsway Business Park, Oldfield Road, Hampton, Middlesex TW12 2HD, UK
Tel: +44 (0)20 8481 7200 **Fax:** +44 (0)20 8941 5548
Email: info@outoftheark.com www.outoftheark.com